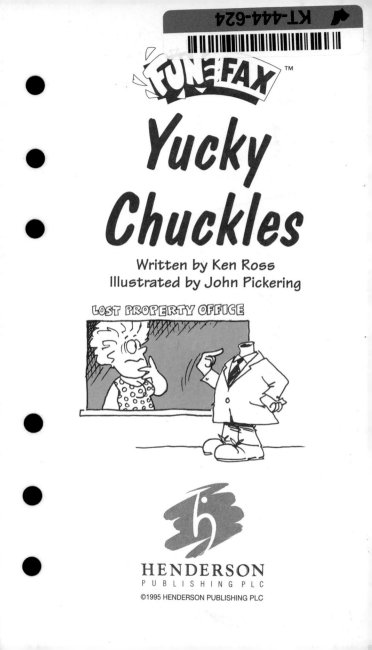

FUNFAX™

Yucky Chuckles

Written by Ken Ross
Illustrated by John Pickering

HENDERSON
PUBLISHING PLC

©1995 HENDERSON PUBLISHING PLC

A

A skunk was sleeping by the river one day, his tail dangling lazily in the water.

Suddenly, a huge fish popped out of the water and grabbed the tail.

"Darling," shouted the fish to his wife. "Look, I've caught this one hook, line and stinker!"

What did the skunk say when the wind changed direction?

"It's all coming back to me now."

TRUE OR FALSE?

The Stink Bomb was invented in 1917 by the German civil engineer Heindrick von Stinkenhoff. He was working for a bridge building company in Holland when by accident he stumbled across his idea. While his team were digging the foundations of a

bridge that was to span a school yard, it unearthed a huge crate filled with Roman underwear. As the underwear was unpacked an overwhelming stink exuded from the crate. Three of his team died of suffocation. Von Stinkenhoff took the underwear back to Germany where he carried out several experiments. Surprisingly he discovered that it was the elastic waistbands in the undergarments that had reacted violently with the muddy soil where his team had been digging. Eventually he boiled two tons of elastic with half a ton of mud from the site of the bridge. Von Stinkenhoff was overcome by fumes, and he died three days later in a Munich hospital.

EX-LEGION SURPLUS

THIS CASE STINKS, NURSE!

See page 24 for the astonishing answer.

The boy stood on the burning deck;
His feet were full of blisters.
The flames came up and burnt his pants
And now he wears his sister's.

The boy stood on the burning deck,
His heart was all a-quiver.
He gave a cough;
His leg fell off
And floated down the river.

YOU'D BETTER HOP IT!

Why do maggots live in cream cakes? So fishermen can't find them.

What is all at sea in a dustbin? A bin liner.

Why do policemen follow people with measles? Because they like doing spot checks.

Who is the smelliest musician? The bloke on the trumpet.

What do smellies with a spring in their step like playing? Ping-pong.

What do you call a kid with greasy hair? Chip.

There was a young fellow named Clyde
Who once at a funeral was spied.
When asked who was dead
He smilingly said,
"I don't know - I just came for the ride!"

A cannibal chief of Penzance
Ate an uncle and two of his aunts,
And then a large piece
Of his least favourite niece;
And now he can't button his pants.

A young custard pie went out. He didn't return and his mum rang the police. 'He's committed a crime,' said the policeman. We've got him in custody.'

The young custard pie was released on bail. When his mum got him home she said, "I'm discustard with you.'

Why have custard pies got brown specks on?

Acheeww! I don't know.

What's sometimes poorly but you can never tell?
A custard pie with jaundice.

What happens if you upset a pustard?
You make a pustard cry.

ARM PIT - a place where you dig for arms.

DETESTABLE - a table where you eat deteses.

FODDER - a bloke who fods.

MOUTHWASH - a place to take mouths for washing.

SECRETE - how to say secret in French.

DISGUSTING - the opposite of 'that gusting'.

TOOTHACHE - twice as much as one thache.

QUEASY - an easy question.

OFFENCE - what goes round a garden.

SQUELCH - a person who comes from Sqwales.

GOO - baby talk as in goo-goo.

RANCID - past tense of Sid having been running.

Perspire - where church dwellers keep their money.

Blackhead - a dead match.

A mum is happy
changing a baby's nappy

A mum is glum
stuffing the chicken's bum

A mum does more
than scrubbing a floor

A mum can't choose
to scrape mud from shoes

A mum cleans grease
and plates of mushy peas

A mum wipes dishes
and gives dad kisses

A mum can't wish
to leave the rubbish

A mum demands
you have clean hands

So let mum moan
when you get home

Or the yukky chores
might just be yours!

There was an old man of St Bees
Who was stung on the arm by a wasp.
When asked "Does it hurt?"
He replied "No, it doesn't -
I'm so glad it wasn't a hornet."

Willie built a guillotine,
Tried it out on sister Jean.
Said mother as she got the mop
"These messy games have got to stop!"

Mary had a little lamb
She tied it to a pylon.
A thousand volts shot up its bum
And turned its wool to nylon.

Mary had a little lamb
She ate it with mint sauce.
Now everywhere that Mary goes
The lamb goes too, of course.

Mary had a wrist watch;
She swallowed it one day.
Now Mary's taking laxatives
To pass the time away.

What has six wheels and flies? A dustbin wagon.

DON'T BUG ME, OK?

What would you say if I told you there were two fish fighting outside? Codswallop.

A fly and his grandfather landed on a bald man's head.

The grandfather turned to his junior and sighed: "When I was your age, this was only a footpath."

How would you describe an angry flea? Hopping mad.

What's green and goes round in circles? A frog in a tumble drier.

Doctor, Doctor,
I keep seeing a spinning fly.
Don't worry, that's just a bug
that's going round.

What's green and
good at maths?
A bogey with a
calculator.

What's green and
highly explosive?
A frog with a stick
of dynamite.

What do a nose
bleed and a potato
have in common?
Neither of them
can fly a plane.

What's crunchy and
furry and makes noises when
you pour milk on it?
Mice crispies.

Smelly socks and big red spots
Germs that live in slime
Brains that bounce and goo that rots
Are all good friends of mine.

Wax from ears and niffy fumes
Fungus that is furry
Dog-breath soup and foisty plumes
Are recipes for curry.

Slush, saliva, suet, sweat
And moss that grows on fingers
Disgusting stains and rancid meat
Green gunge and shocking stinkers.

Foul and gammy handkerchiefs
And plagues that live in compost
Cow-pat pies with mould that leaves
You sniffing at a lamp post.

Sing along with the yukky song,
Of all things pongy and piquant,
Don't be surprised, if before your eyes
Your mum calls you 'deliquant!'

What do you give to a constipated budgie? Chirrup of figs.

Did you hear about the two blood cells? They loved in vein.

Doctor, Doctor, will this cream clear up my spots? I never make rash promises.

How did the murderer clean up his mess? With a victim cleaner.

What has fifty legs and can't walk? Half a centipede.

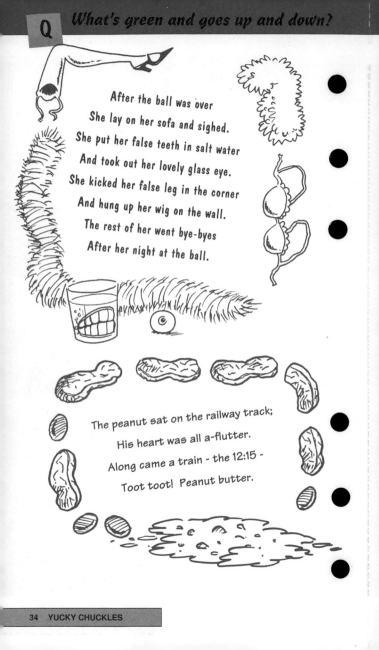

After the ball was over
She lay on her sofa and sighed.
She put her false teeth in salt water
And took out her lovely glass eye.
She kicked her false leg in the corner
And hung up her wig on the wall.
The rest of her went bye-byes
After her night at the ball.

The peanut sat on the railway track;
His heart was all a-flutter.
Along came a train - the 12:15 -
Toot toot! Peanut butter.

A man he lived by the sewer
And by the sewer he died.
And at the coroner's inquest
They named it sewer-side.

There's a cross-eyed woman in our town,
She's boss-eyed, that's a fact;
And every time the lady cries
The tears roll down her back.

What's black and white and red at the bottom? A badger with nappy rash.

What's black and white and can't turn round in a corridor? A nun with a javelin in her handbag.

What's worse than a frog in the throat? A toad in der dose.

What's white and goes 'baaa-aaaa-aa'? A sheep falling off a cliff.

What's green and white and swings through trees? Tarzan's hankie.

Live green slime is discovered in Mexico. It is called Pedro and wins the Nobel Prize for Literature with its novel about basket weaving.

In England the world's greatest smelly sock nicker is nabbed. His house is filled with 25 million odd smelly socks. He is ordered to wear stick-on wellies for the rest of his life and he is given a plastic nose transplant.

Custard rain falls in Central Australia forming a lake three hundred miles wide. Every Australian is invited to bring a sponge pudding so the whole country can take part in a giant feast.

In Canada nine mounties and their horses are imprisoned below earth by a bog monster. After a ransom of six tons of chocolate is paid, the mounties are released. They continue to send the monster chocolates by undertaker, "to keep him sweet".

CHOCS

ALL BECAUSE THE MONSTER LOVES NINE WAYS!

A slug called Sybil becomes president of the United States. She resides under a big brick in Central Park, New York, and takes her pet hamster Nigel everywhere she goes. By the end of the Century she has decreed that no human may move further than half a mile a day.

MADAM PRESIDENT

A

What do you call a deer with its legs chopped off and its eyes poked out? Still no idea.

Why did the punk cross the road? It was stapled to the chicken.

What's green and wobbly? A seasick pig.

What do you do if an elephant sneezes? Get out of the way.

What do you get hanging from trees? Sore arms.

What's blue, likes peanuts, and weighs a lot? An ink-stained elephant.

When grandma visits you, my dears,
Be as good as you can be.
Don't put hot crumpets in her ears
Or beetles in her tea.

Don't sew a pattern on her cheek
With cotton or with silk.
Don't call her naughty names in Greek
Or spray her face with milk.

Don't drive a staple in her foot;
Don't stick pins in her head.
And oh, I beg you, do not put
Great spiders in her bed.

These things are not considered kind;
They worry her, and tease.
Such cruelty is not refined -
It always fails to please.

Be good to grandma, little peeps,
Whatever else you do;
And then she'll grow to be - perhaps -
More tolerant of you.

A

Boils Ivor Greenhead

The Spot
Willie Pickett

Dribbling Sally Vate

Embarrassing Rashes
Madam Acne

Scars Mark Pocks

Awful Colds
Noah Zizblocked

Rat Soup Rowe, Dent & Bowl

Sick As A Parrot Polly Gipping

Rotting Eggs
Michelle Broken

Exploring Intestines Ann Innard

Coming Up Trumps Lottie Beans

Never Get Washed Phil Feedevil